THE HAIRY-NOSED WOMBATS
FIND A NEW HOME

JACKIE FRENCH

Illustrated by SUE deGENNARO

Angus&Robertson
An imprint of HarperCollins*Children's Books*

To whiskery wildlife everywhere, and those who care for them.
And Jack. xxxx — Jackie French

For Sally — Sue deGennaro

Angus & Robertson
An imprint of HarperCollins*Children's Books* Australia

First published in Australia in 2014
This edition published in 2015
by HarperCollins*Publishers* Australia Pty Limited
ABN 36 009 913 517
harpercollins.com.au

Text copyright © Jackie French, 2014
Illustrations copyright © Sue deGennaro, 2014

HarperCollins*Publishers*
Level 13, 201 Elizabeth Street, Sydney, NSW 2000, Australia
Unit D1, 63 Apollo Drive, Rosedale, Auckland 0632 New Zealand
A 53, Sector 57, Noida, UP, India
77–85 Fulham Palace Road, London, W6 8JB, United Kingdom
2 Bloor Street East, 20th floor, Toronto, Ontario M4W 1A8, Canada
195 Broadway, New York NY 10007, USA

National Library of Australia Cataloguing-in-Publication entry:

French, Jackie, author.
    The hairy-nosed wombats find a new home / Jackie French ;
    Sue De Gennaro, illustrator.
    ISBN: 978 0 7322 9548 6 (hardback)
    ISBN: 978 0 7322 9550 9 (paperback)
    For primary school age.
    Southern hairy-nosed wombat – Australia – Juvenile fiction.
    Wombats – Habitations – Juvenile fiction.
    Wombats – Australia – Juvenile fiction.
    De Gennaro, Sue, illustrator.

A823.3

Cover and internal design by Natalie Winter
The illustrations in this book were created in watercolour and collage
Colour reproduction by Graphic Print Group, Adelaide
Printed and bound in China by RR Donnelley on 140g Golden Sun

5 4 3 2 1   15 16 17 18

The Wombat Foundation is a charitable organisation set up to support activities that aim to bring the Northern Hairy-nosed Wombat back from the brink of extinction.

The Northern Hairy-nosed Wombat is one of the world's rarest species – it is rarer than the Giant Panda.

We work hard to make a difference by funding research and conservation activities, and raising the profile of the species, but we also have a lot of fun along the way!

Jacqui Mills
Director, The Wombat Foundation, 2014

Once there were **176 wombats**, all with whiskery noses.

They were the only Northern Hairy-noses left **in the world!**

What if **fire** burnt their land?

What if **flood** washed away their burrows?

The only Hairy-nose home might be gone **forever**.

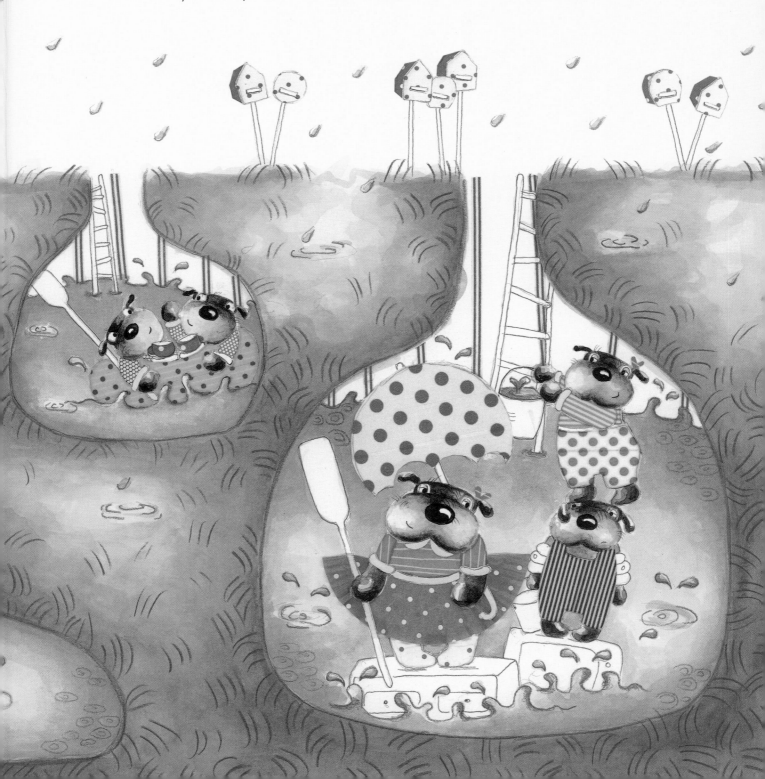

So some of the whiskery wombats needed to
leave the burrows they had always known.

They had to find another **happy home** for Hairy-noses!

But **where** could the new home be?

It must be out of **flood** reach.

It must have **tasty grass**.

And be **so good** that Hairy-noses would have wispy, wild babies, too.

It was time for one wondrous wombat adventure!

Five big, brave boys set out.

It was a **long** way for whiskery wombats to travel.

Would the new place be as wonderful as they had hoped?

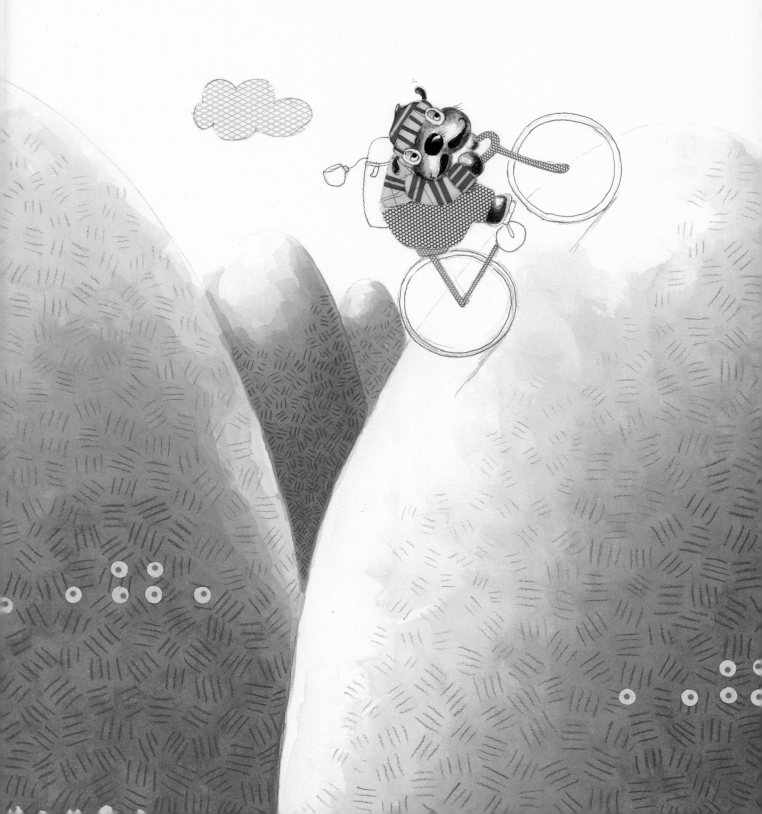

IT WAS!

The Hairy-nosed boys gobbled
the good green grass.

They dug deep burrows in the sandy soil.

And then ...

THE GIRLS ARRIVED!

More whiskery wombats came
from the old home.

And at last ...

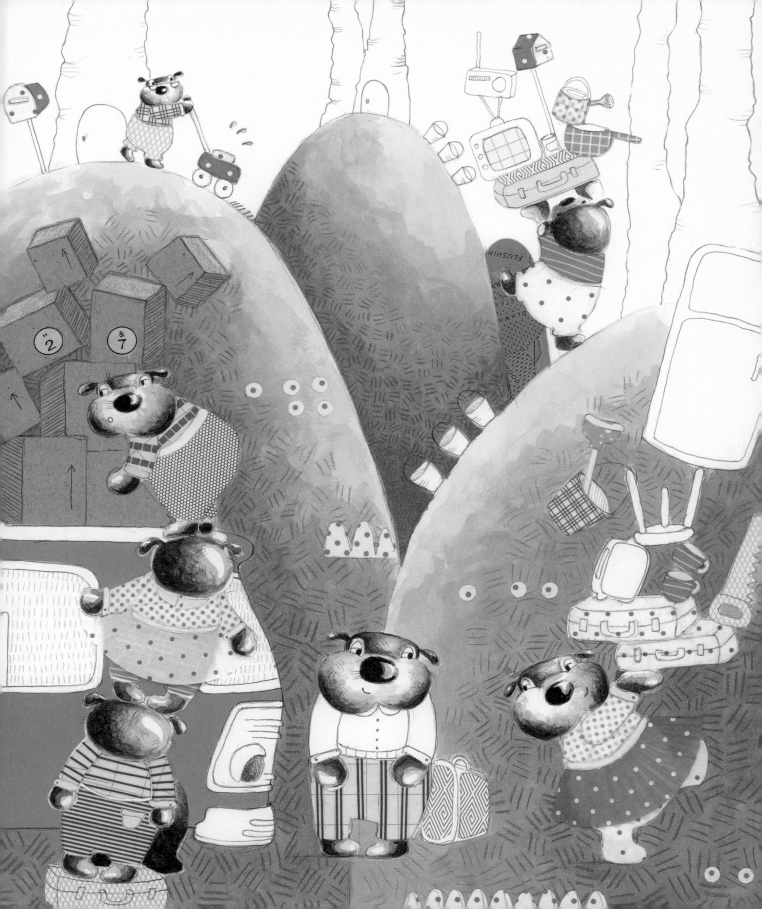

The most special,

        wiggly,

            wobbly,

                  wonderful

                            wombat of them all!

The world would have
more Northern Hairy-noses ...
and more happy homes
for whiskery wildlife ...

FOREVER.

THE TRUE HISTORY OF THE HAIRY-NOSES

The Northern Hairy-nosed Wombat is one of the world's most endangered animals, even more endangered than the panda.

Long ago, there were many Hairy-noses in Australia. Then, when sheep and cattle were brought here, they ate the wombats' grass and drank their water. The cattle's heavy hooves made the soil too hard to dig burrows, and made the burrow entrances collapse. The buffel grass brought in to feed the new animals was often too high for Hairy-noses to eat. Introduced diseases, like mange and toxoplasmosis, and wild dogs killed many wombats, too.

By 1930, it seemed as though the world had lost Hairy-noses forever. Then, in 1937, a few wombats were found at Epping Forest in central Queensland.

From 1971 to1974 Epping Forest National Park was established, with 3,160 hectares preserved to help protect the wombats. Cattle were taken out of the park. Later, in 2002, volunteers raised enough money to enclose the wombats' home in a high fence to keep out wild dogs, and to install feeding and water stations. The only people allowed to visit the park from that time onwards were scientists to study and count the wombats, as well as caretakers and volunteers to slash the buffel grass to provide short grass for wombats to eat, to mend the fence and look after the water stations and other maintenance.

But a long drought meant that there still weren't many young wombats. In the 1980s there were only about 35 Hairy-noses left in the world. More than half were males, and many of the females were thought too old to have babies. It seemed that the Hairy-noses would soon become extinct.

At last the rains came. Baby wombats were born. And more. And more!

By 2010 there were 176 Hairy-nosed Wombats. But the wombats were still far from safe. What if a flood washed out their burrows, fire burnt their land, or a new disease infected the colony?

In July 2009, five Northern Hairy-nosed Wombats were moved to a new home at the Richard Underwood Nature Refuge at Yarran Downs, 70 kilometres north of St George in Queensland. St George is one of the few locations where Northern Hairy-nosed Wombats have been officially recorded, although about a hundred years ago.

The wombats' new home was fenced, with ready-made burrows and feed and water stations.

The first five wombats were all males. Females were too wary to be easily caught. And if the relocation didn't work, none of the precious females who might have baby wombats would be lost. Over the next year, another ten wombats, including females, arrived in three separate airlifts.

And then in March 2011, a baby Hairy-nosed Wombat was seen at the Refuge – and then, in April, another one. It appeared the Hairy-noses had decided their new home was good.

Northern Hairy-nosed Wombats are still critically endangered. But at last it seems that with the help of researchers, volunteers, farmers like Ed and Gabi Underwood who donated the land for the reserve, the mining company Xstrata who provided funds, and the many thousands of people who have donated money to help research or set up the reserves, one of the world's most endangered species may be saved. Scientists and other wombat experts are now looking for a third 'new home' for Hairy-noses, a large one where hundreds or even many thousands of wombats can live and breed.

The 2013 census has just been completed at Epping Forest, with volunteers taking hair samples from the burrows to test the wombats' DNA to find out exactly how many Hairy-noses there are. The results won't be known until after this book is printed, but it looks like there are now at least two hundred Hairy-noses at Epping Forest, with many babies, as well as three baby Hairy-noses at the Richard Underwood Nature Refuge.

There is still so much we don't know about Northern Hairy-noses, or their wombat relatives. Bare-nosed Wombats are under threat from mange, wild dogs, toxoplasmosis spread by feral cats, road deaths and competition from sheep, cattle and feral animals like goats. Southern Hairy-nosed Wombats are also being desperately affected by toxic weeds.

The tale of the Hairy-noses is important. It shows that a species that so very nearly became extinct can be saved just by providing them with a safe place to live, with good food and water. That way endangered animals can do what they do best, living happily, and breeding babies, so our planet can continue to have the beauty and diversity of many, many species – including the Hairy-noses.

Jackie French's proceeds from this book will be used to help wombat research. If you would like to help too, either by raising money for research or wombat refuges, or helping as a volunteer, go to www.wombatfoundation.com.au where you'll also find much more information about the fascinating world of Hairy-noses.

On Hairy-nosed Day each May you, too, could put on a hairy nose to Wear Whiskers for Wildlife, and raise funds to help wombats.

AUTHOR'S NOTE

I love wombats. I love the way their front half goes one way and their back half goes another when they walk. I love the way wombats grin. I love Bare-nosed Wombats and Southern Hairy-nosed Wombats. I love Northern Hairy-nosed Wombats, too, even though I have never met one. You don't need to meet an animal to love it.

Humans need to share this planet with other species, not just because it is their home as well, but because each species helps keep the world a good place. In our valley, wombats help to maintain the natural environment by recycling the nutrients in the things they eat back into the soil via their scats, so as old plants die new ones can grow to replace them.

Wombats teach us a different way of looking at the world. Wombats are shortsighted but their sense of smell is perhaps 10,000 times more acute than a dog's — and a dog's is 10,000 times keener than ours.

Wombats don't use spoken words, but they understand each other and us, by smells, and also by sounds. Years ago, I discovered that if I sang, the wombats knew where I was and that also, from the tone of my voice, I wasn't going to hurt them. Most days, now, I track wombats in the bush and orchards around my home, watching them and studying them.

The story of the Hairy-noses of Epping teaches us that endangered species can survive, if we care enough to give them a safe place to live. My life has been enormously richer because it has been shared with other species. May your lives be as rich in friendships with many other species, too.

Jackie French, 2014

ILLUSTRATOR'S NOTE

For as long as I can remember, I have always walked the streets with my head down, potentially leading me into telephone poles but mostly in the pursuit of finding things: wrappers, handwritten notes, and ticket stubs. All the papers I have gleaned and gathered are stored in boxes in my studio. Whenever I approach the artwork for a new book I reach for those boxes of collected paper. Often it is only one or two pieces of paper that actually make it into my final artwork, but they are essential to the overall feel of the book.

The artwork in this book is a mixture of watercolour and collage. The wombats are painted in watercolour but their clothes are made from a collection of coloured masking tape, the inside pattern of envelopes and graph paper. In this book I dressed each wombat as you would a cardboard cut-out doll with paper dresses. Using this technique gave me the chance to experiment with endless combinations of shirts and pants until the perfect combination was reached. And just for the record, dressing a wombat took a lot longer than I expected!

Sue deGennaro, 2014